For Alexa Rose,
Amelia Rose
& Addison Rose
-A.E.

For my mother, &
the doctors & nurses
at Liberec hospital
-M.J-L.

NAME THAT

Amelia Edwards

First published 2009 by Walker Books Ltd
87 Vauxhall Walk, London SE11 5HJ

10 9 8 7 6 5 4 3 2 1

Text © 2009 Amelia Edwards
Illustrations © 2009 Martina Jirankova-Limbrick
Poem on page 26 © 2009 Jamie Michalak

The right of Amelia Edwards and Martina Jirankova-Limbrick
to be identified as author and illustrator respectively of this
work has been asserted by them in accordance with the
Copyright, Designs and Patents Act 1988

This book has been typeset in Shinn.

Printed in China.

British Library Cataloguing in Publication Data: a catalogue
record for this book is available from the British Library

ISBN 978-0-7445-6590-4

www.walker.co.uk

DINOSAUR! A Puzzle Adventure

Illustrated by Martina Jirankova-Limbrick

Do you love dinosaurs? Abba, the girl in this book, does.
She has dinosaur models, dinosaur books – and now her dad
has given her a dinosaur puzzle poster. (Her little dog Dash likes it too!)
Take the jacket off your book, unfold the edges
and find your own dinosaur puzzle poster. Look out
for the dinosaur name stickers too!

Are you ready to play? Turn the page,
so the game can begin!

WALKER BOOKS
AND SUBSIDIARIES
LONDON · BOSTON · SYDNEY · AUCKLAND

It's early in the morning and Abba is very excited. She's looking at her brand-new dinosaur poster. It has sixteen pictures of dinosaurs on it and she wants to find out their names and fill them in, so she can show her dad at breakfast.

Abba spots a **TYRANNOSAURUS REX** just like the one in her picture book, a **STEGOSAURUS** like the big model she has and a **TRICERATOPS** like the picture on her wall.

Can you find the three dinosaurs on *your* poster? Look for the stickers with their names on and stick them underneath each one.

Can you see another dinosaur hidden in Abba's room? *Hint:* look over a lion and under a clock.

Abba lives on an island called Rosa Turuso. On some special mornings like this one, when the moon and the sun both shine in the sky, things come alive for a time – and Rosa Turuso is full of magic...

First to come alive is Abba's friend, Hattah – a hat! She hovers over the poster. "There's a **DIPLODOCUS**, like the one on my shelf," she says.

"How can we find out the names of all the other dinosaurs?" asks Abba.

"We'll visit Mr Lion at the library," says Hattah. "He knows everything."

Dash barks with excitement and – *WHOOSH!* – magic Hattah makes Abba a travelling suit, and turns herself into a balloon!

And so the three friends set out on an adventure...

Did you spot the DIPLODOCUS on the last page? Find its name sticker and match it to the one on your poster.

Hattah turns on her brim lights
and off they go,
gently down Big Hill ...

zig-zagging
through
Crooked Village ...

gliding
over
Bookway Bridge ...

then up to
Pinetree Pass
and Mr Lion's library.

SWISSSSSH!
Hattah's a hat again!

"Good morning," says Mr Lion, looking up from his book. "What can I do for you?"

When Abba tells him about her search, he wants to help. "Let's go to the Science Reading Room," he says.

"This book shows a **BRACHIOSAURUS**," Mr Lion says. "And your book shows a **BAROSAURUS**. Behind us on the board is an **ANKYLOSAURUS**."

Can you find the dinosaurs Mr Lion shows Abba on your poster? Can you find their name stickers too?

"Next you should visit my friend Professor Dragonby," says Mr Lion. "He's a palaeontologist – a dinosaur expert. If you go now, you may catch him at Dino-maze Park."

AMAZING
DINOSAUR models!

Created by Professor Dragonby

See them at Dino-maze Park and Dinomore Museum

Abba and Hattah get ready to go, but where is Dash? Abba whistles his favourite tune...

Can you find Dash for Abba? Who else can you find?

Dash wriggles out of the poster where he's been sleeping. Hattah giggles but Abba just hugs him.

"Fly west and you'll soon see Dino-maze Park," calls Mr Lion.

"Goodbye!" says Abba. "Thank you."

Hattah twirls round to become a balloon again, and the three friends are soon on their way.

Abba looks down from the basket. "There's a BIG dinosaur!" she says.

"**GIGANOTOSAURUS**," Hattah reads off the sign. "That's a good name for it."

"Lucky it's only a bush!" says Abba, as they land softly beside it.

Can you match the GIGANOTOSAURUS to the one on your poster? Find its name sticker and stick it underneath.

GIGANOTOSAURUS

It's very quiet in Dino-maze Park, and there's no sign of the Professor.

"Is anybody here?" Abba shouts.

"We are, we are!" Suddenly seven little lizards appear.

"We're the Dancing Lizards. We work with Professor Dragonby." And they introduce themselves...

"Now you see us," the lizards call. "Now you don't!" And then they vanish.

"Come back!" Abba calls. "We want to meet Professor Dragonby."

Can you help Abba, Dash and Hattah find the seven lizards? *Hint:* **try matching their pictures above to the shapes hidden in the hedges.**

"My name is Cha Cha,"

"There's one ... two, three, four ... five, six ... seven lizards!" counts Hattah.

"You found us!" shouts Cha Cha.

"Now will you take us to meet the Professor?" Abba asks.

"He's in the middle!" says Cha Cha.

"The middle of what?" asks Hattah.

"This amazing maze!" says Samba.

Hattah floats up to take a look.

"But how will we find our way through it?" asks Abba.

Can you see which path the friends should take?

They reach the middle at last!

"Hello," says Professor Dragonby. "Can I help?"

"Yes, please," Abba says. "Mr Lion sent us."

"You must come to Dinomore Museum," the Professor says, when he hears about the search. "We're getting an exhibition ready there. Some of the dinosaur models we're making may be the ones on your poster."

"But first meet **ALLOSAURUS**!" calls Tango.

Dash growls.

"Don't worry," says Abba. "It's only a bush like the other one."

Can you match the ALLOSAURUS to the one on your poster? Find its name sticker and stick it underneath. How many dinosaurs do you still have left to name?

Hattah and Abba offer the lizards a ride to the museum. Dash goes in Professor Dragonby's pocket.

As they get closer a creature flies up to greet the Professor.

"Who's that?" Abba asks.

"Marianne," Samba says. "The Professor invented her. She's a robot pteranodon."

"I don't think she's one of the ones on my poster," says Abba.

"Pteranodons aren't dinosaurs," Samba tells her, "though they lived at the same time."

"There's a dinosaur over there, Abba, look!" Hattah calls.

"That's a mountain!" Cha Cha says, laughing. "Mount **SPINOSAURUS**."

Look carefully – can you match the shape of the mountain to the SPINOSAURUS on your poster? Look for its name sticker and stick it underneath.

They land on the roof of Dinomore Museum.

"Here are the models we've made for the exhibition," says the Professor.

"Which ones do you know already, Abba?" asks Mambo.

Look at the eight dinosaur models. Which four do *you* know already?

Abba helps the lizards paint name signs for the models in their studio. They sing a little dinosaur song while they work:

> "*Tricera-goes,*
> *Tricera-stops,*
> *Tricera-bottoms,*
> *Tricera-tops!*"

Try reading the dinosaur signs. Can you finish saying the names of the ones you know?

Back on the rooftop, the lizards put up the signs.

"Are they in the right places?" asks Samba.

Abba stands back to look.

"Uh-oh!" she says. "Two of them need to be switched!"

Can you spot the two signs that are mixed up? *Hint:* look at the picture shapes of the dinosaurs on the signs.

TRICERATOPS

STEGOSAURUS

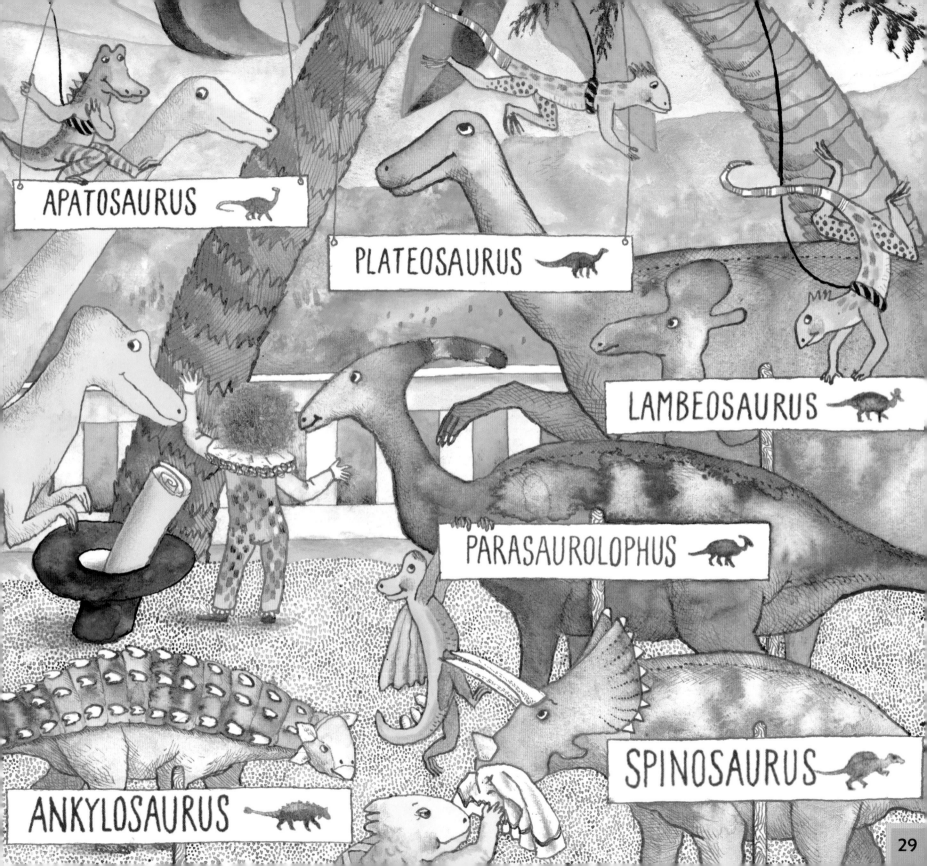

APATOSAURUS

PLATEOSAURUS

LAMBEOSAURUS

PARASAUROLOPHUS

ANKYLOSAURUS

SPINOSAURUS

Luckily, when the Professor comes to check, everything's in order!

"Have you found the names of any more dinosaurs?" he asks.

"Yes!" says Abba, looking at her poster.

"There's a **LAMBEOSAURUS**," says Hattah.

"And a **PLATEOSAURUS**," says Rumba.

"And an **APATOSAURUS** and a **PARASAUROLOPHUS**..." says Abba. "Only two left to find."

"Well done!" the Professor smiles. "Now come along to my workshop, I have something to give you before you go."

Can you spot the four new dinosaurs on *your* poster? Find their name stickers and stick them on.

SPINOSAURUS

STEGOSAURUS

APATOSAURUS

PLATEOSAURUS

LAMBEOSAURUS

PARASAUROLOPHUS

ANKYLOSAURUS

TRICERATOPS

Marianne is sitting on the Professor's workbench. Beside her is another robot.

"I've just made a friend for her," the Professor says, as he rummages in a drawer. "I think I'll call her Marybeth."

"They're exactly the same!" says Tango.

"Not exactly," says the Professor. "There are some differences. Ah – here we are."

He gives Abba a map. "This is the island of Rosa Turuso," he tells her. "Look at it carefully. You may find one of the answers you need right under your nose!"

Can you spot seven differences between the pteranodon robots? Which one is Marianne? *Hint:* **look on page 25.**

"Goodbye! Thank you!" call the friends, as they float up into the sky.

"We want to give you something too," Cha Cha calls. "We'll send it special delivery!"

Abba studies the map. "Rosa Turuso is shaped just like a dinosaur's head, Hattah! It looks like one of the last two dinosaurs on the poster. But what is its name?"

"Hm," says Hattah, thinking. "Professor Dragonby said the answer would be under your nose... What happens if you scramble the letters of ROSA TURUSO?"

"TO-RO—" Abba tries.

"That's it!" Hattah says. "**TOROSAURUS** is a dinosaur name."

Can you match the island shape on the map to one of the last two dinosaurs on your poster? Now stick its name sticker on.

CROOKED
VILLAGE

BOOKWAY
BRIDGE

PINETREE
PASS

DINOMORE
MUSEUM

ROSA TURUSC

ROSA TURUS

"We still have one last name to find," Abba says, as they land gently home.

"Look at your picture book," Hattah says. "I wonder who turned the page?"

Abba looks at the page and then at her poster. "**IGUANADON**. There it is!"

"We've done it," sighs Hattah on her shelf. The moon has set and it's time for her to be only a hat again.

Abba can hear her family getting breakfast ready. She can't wait to show her dad the finished poster. But would he believe her if she told him about her magic adventure?

Then she sees a package on the table...

How did it get there? She opens the envelope. "It's a present from the Dancing Lizards, Hattah!"

But Hattah is fast asleep...

Can you see who visited Abba's room? Now turn the page. Is there a present for you too?

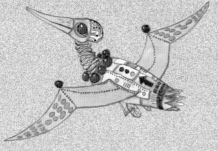